THE HUMAN BODY

INSTRUCTIONS

1 Open the front flap on the VR viewer. Bring the top and side flaps up and over. The side flaps attach to the side of the viewer with Velcro.

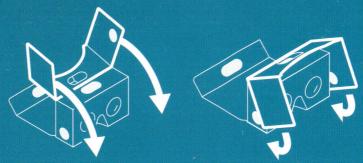

2 Download PI VR Human Body, available on the App Store or Google Play. Direct links to the store locations are found at: pilbooks.com/PIVRHumanBody.

3 Launch the app. You may be asked to calibrate your viewer by scanning the QR code found on the bottom of the viewer itself. You will be able to change your viewer settings later in the options menu.

4 After calibrating your viewer, you will be prompted to scan the QR code found to the right to verify your possession of this book.

5 You will see a double image of the human bloodstream on your phone. Insert your smartphone into the front compartment of the VR viewer. The line between the two images should line up with the notch at the center point of the viewer, between the two lenses. If your screen seems blurry, make sure the smartphone is aligned precisely with the center of the viewer. Adjusting the phone left or right a few millimeters can make a big difference. The tilt of the viewer and the phone can also affect how the screen looks to you.

6 Look around to explore! PI VR Human Body does not require a lever or remote control. You control each interaction with your gaze. When you see a loading circle, keep your gaze focused until it loads fully to access videos, slideshows, and games.

Loading

7 Gaze at the X to close out of video, slideshow, or game screens.

Exit

pi
Publications International, Ltd.

Get the App!

This book is enhanced by an app that can be downloaded from the App Store or Google Play*. Apps are available to download at no cost. Once you've downloaded the app to your smartphone**, use the QR code found on page 1 of this book to access an immersive, 360° virtual reality environment. Then slide the phone into the VR viewer and you're ready to go.

Compatible Operating Systems

- Android 4.1 (JellyBean) or later

- iOS 8.0 or later

Compatible Phones

The app is designed to work with smartphones with a screen size of up to 6 inches. Removing your device from its case may provide a better fit in the viewer. If your smartphone meets the above operating system requirements and has gyroscope functionality it should support GoogleVR. Publications International, Ltd. has developed and tested this software with the following devices:

- Google Nexus 5, Google Nexus 5X

- Motorola Moto Z

- Apple iPhone 6, Apple iPhone 6 Plus, Apple iPhone 7, Apple iPhone 8, Apple iPhone X

- Samsung Galaxy S6, Samsung Galaxy S6 Edge, Samsung Galaxy S7, Samsung Galaxy S8

Caution

The viewer should not be exposed to moisture or extreme temperatures. The viewer is not water resistant. It is potentially combustible if the lenses are left facing a strong light source.

Apple, the Apple logo and iPhone are trademarks of Apple Inc., registered in the U.S. and other countries. App Store is a service mark of Apple Inc., registered in the U.S. and other countries. Google Play and the Google Play logo are trademarks of Google Inc. Nexus is a trademark of Google Inc. Samsung and Galaxy are trademarks of Samsung Electronics Co. Ltd. MOTOROLA and the Stylized M logo are registered trademarks of Motorola Trademark Holding, LLC.

 Publications International, Ltd.

For inquiries email: customer_service@pubint.com

ISBN: 978-1-64030-328-7

Manufactured in China.

8 7 6 5 4 3 2 1

*We reserve the right to terminate the apps.
**Smartphone not included. Standard data rates may apply to download. Once downloaded, the app does not use data or require Wi-Fi access.

CONTENTS

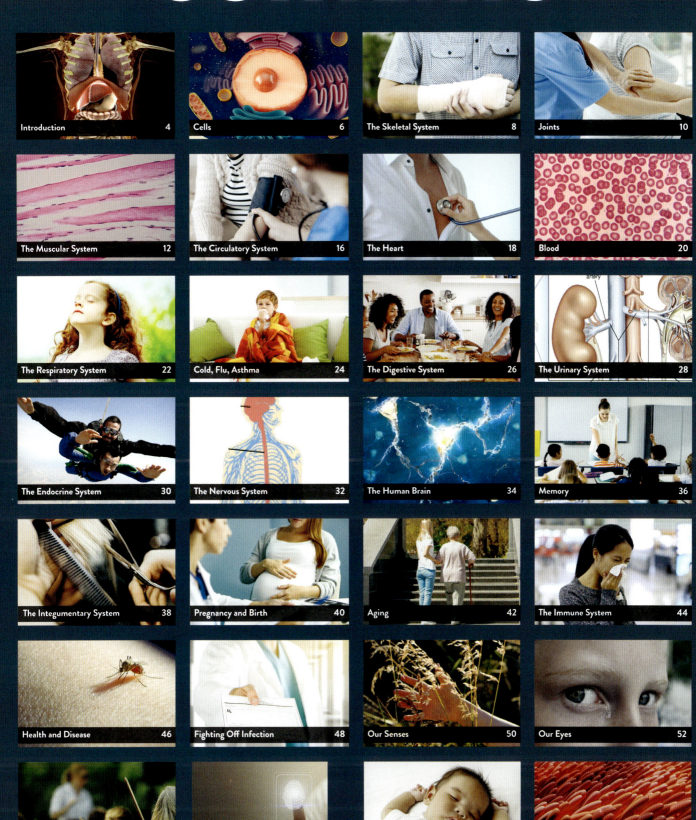

INTRODUCTION

The human body is a combination of parts and systems that work together to perform the necessary functions of life. The body is composed of cells and extracellular materials that are organized into tissues, organs, and organ systems.

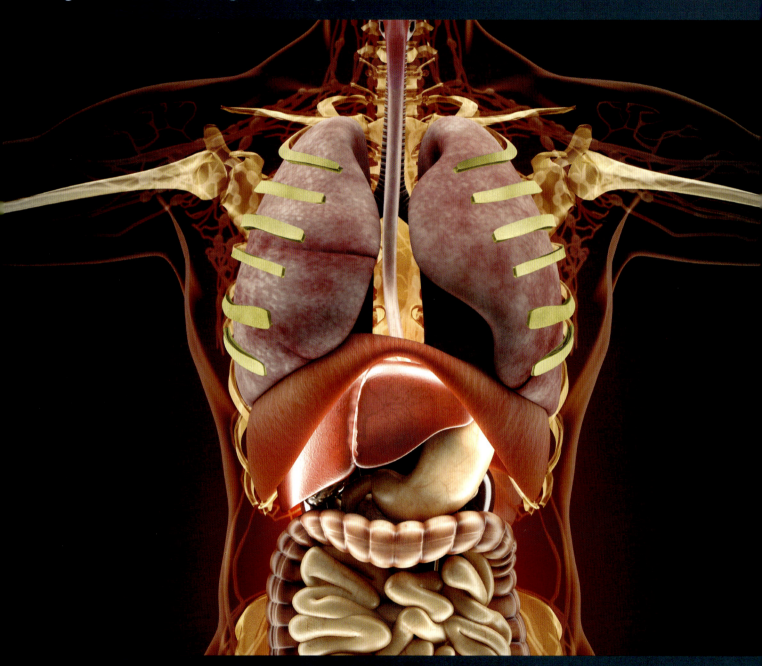

WHAT IS ANATOMY?

To understand the human body it is necessary to know the structure of its parts, what they do, and how they work together. Anatomy is the scientific study of the structure of living things. The study of how the structures function is known as physiology. Scientists find it useful to divide the human body into 11 major systems: skeletal, muscular, circulatory, respiratory, digestive, urinary (excretory), endocrine, nervous, integumentary, reproductive, and immune.

FIVE FAST FACTS

1 Humans are endothermic, or warm-blooded, meaning that their body temperature remains relatively constant regardless of environmental temperature.

2 The human body is composed of water, minerals, and organic compounds (mainly proteins, lipids, carbohydrates, and nucleic acids).

3 Water composes up to 60 percent of the body. It is found outside of cells in body fluids, such as blood and lymph, and in the spaces between tissues.

4 Water also is found inside the cells, where it plays a key role in cellular processes and chemical reactions essential to life.

5 Calcium, phosphorus, sodium, magnesium, and iron are the main inorganic minerals found in the body.

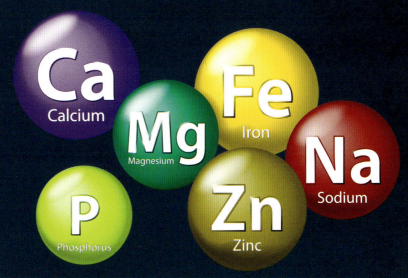

USE THE VR VIEWER AND ASSOCIATED APP

Enhance your experience by using the app! Put your smartphone in the VR viewer to see your immune system in action.

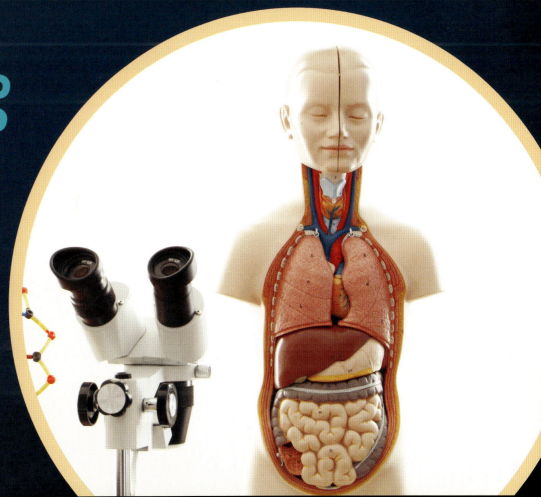

CELLS

The smallest unit of living matter that can exist by itself is the cell. Some organisms, such as bacteria, consist of only a single cell. Others, such as humans, are composed of many billions of cells. Regardless of its shape and size, every cell can perform certain functions on its own. A cell can digest nutrients to provide its own energy. It can also produce new cells by making copies of itself. Most cells do this by dividing. In organisms with many cells, each cell must also cooperate with other cells. To do this, a cell must communicate with its neighbors.

FIVE FAST FACTS

1. Cells exist in a variety of shapes and sizes. Red blood cells are disk-shaped, while some skin cells resemble cubes.

2. Cells normally function with great efficiency, though they are vulnerable to disease.

3. Cell size is usually measured in microns. A micron is equal to about one millionth of a meter, and about 25,000 microns equal 1 inch.

4. The diameter of the average human cell is roughly 10 microns, making it barely visible without a microscope.

5. Human beings are made up of more than 75 trillion cells.

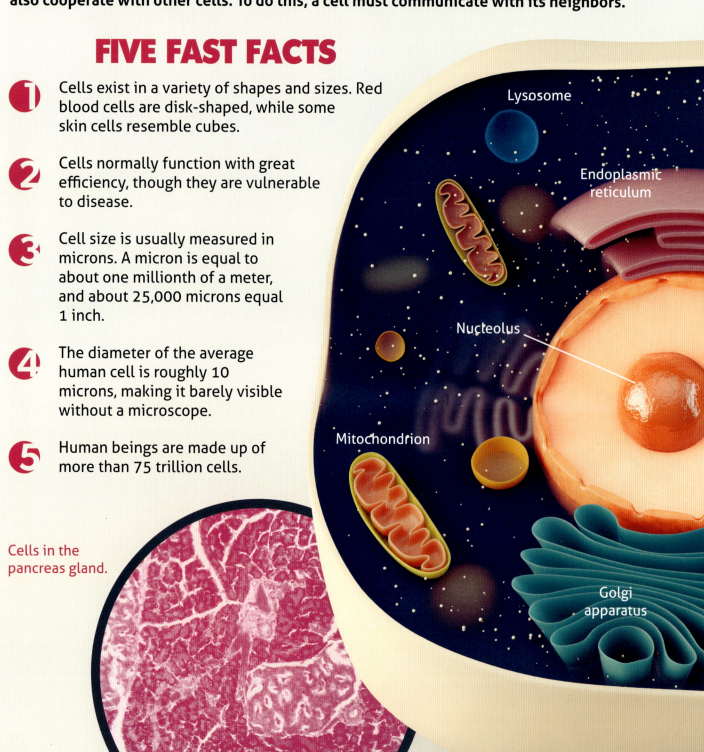

Lysosome

Endoplasmic reticulum

Nucleolus

Mitochondrion

Golgi apparatus

Cells in the pancreas gland.

PARTS OF A CELL

Most cells have three main parts—the cell membrane, the cytoplasm, and the nucleus. The cell membrane is like the skin of the cell. The cytoplasm performs many functions to keep the cell alive. The nucleus can be thought of as the cell's brain.

IN THE CYTOPLASM

The cytoplasm is composed mainly of water, with some solids. Most of the cell's constant work of keeping alive is performed in the cytoplasm. Special organs, called organelles, within the cytoplasm make important substances called proteins. Cells use proteins in most of their chemical processes. Other organelles change food molecules into material needed for energy and growth. A network of tubes transports material within the cell.

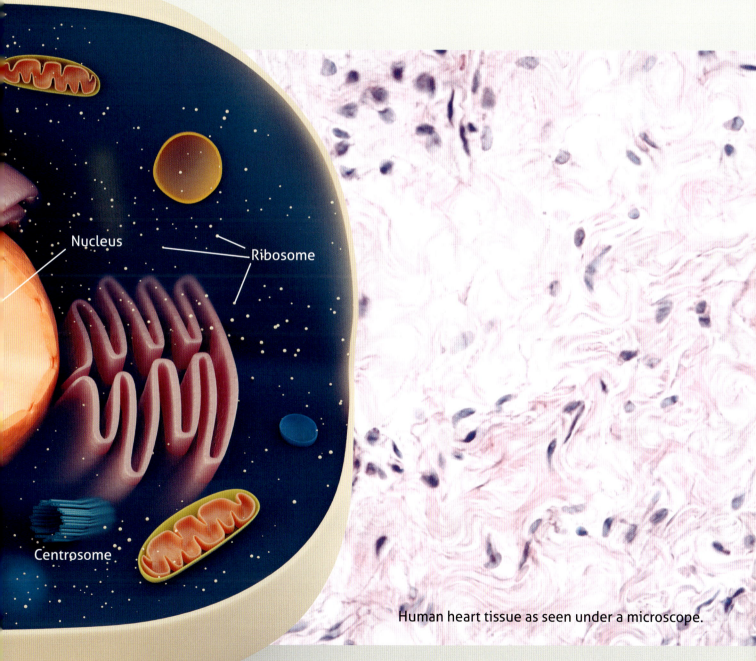

Nucleus

Ribosome

Centrosome

Human heart tissue as seen under a microscope.

THE SKELETAL SYSTEM

The human skeletal system is made of an internal skeleton that serves as a framework for the body. The skeleton consists of bones, joints, and cartilage. The system also includes bands of fibrous connective tissue called ligaments that connect parts of the skeleton and aid movement.

PROTECTING THE BRAIN

The skull is composed of cranial and facial bones. Eight bones unite to enclose the brain within a strong box, the cranium, and to form sockets for the eyes and ears. The face has 14 bones.

WHAT DOES THE SKELETON DO?

The main function of the skeleton is to support and protect the soft tissues and the organs of the body and to provide points of attachment for the muscles that move the body.

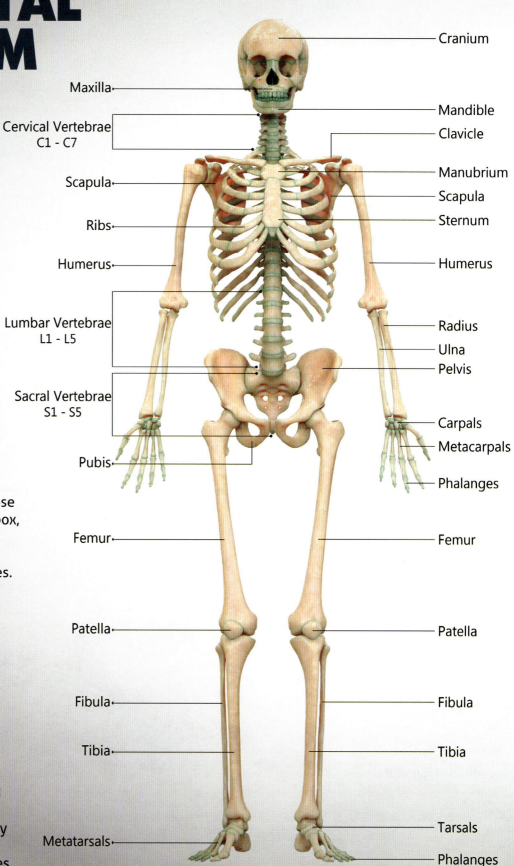

Cranium

Maxilla

Mandible

Clavicle

Cervical Vertebrae C1 - C7

Manubrium

Scapula

Scapula

Sternum

Ribs

Humerus

Humerus

Radius

Lumbar Vertebrae L1 - L5

Ulna

Pelvis

Sacral Vertebrae S1 - S5

Carpals

Metacarpals

Pubis

Phalanges

Femur

Femur

Patella

Patella

Fibula

Fibula

Tibia

Tibia

Tarsals

Metatarsals

Phalanges

HOW MANY BONES?

The human skeleton contains 206 bones of various shapes—long, short, cube-shaped, flat, and irregular. Many of the long bones have an interior space that is filled with bone marrow, a spongy substance involved in the production and destruction of blood cells.

WHAT MAKES UP OUR BONES?

About 60 percent of fully developed bone is mineral (mostly calcium and magnesium). The remainder consists of water and matrix, a protein-rich material that provides a foundation for mineral deposit.

TWO PARTS

The human skeleton is divided into two main parts—the axial skeleton and appendicular skeleton. The axial skeleton consists of the head, neck, and trunk. The appendicular skeleton is made up of the arms and legs.

Like any rigid structure, bone can break. The differences in the breaks and in the rate of healing that occur at different ages reflect the changing makeup of bone over time.

THE BACKBONE

In infants the spine consists of 33 irregular bones, called vertebrae. In adults the nine bones at the lower end of the column have fused into two masses, the upper five uniting to form the sacrum and the remaining four the coccyx. Thus during the greater part of a person's life the backbone consists of 24 vertebrae.

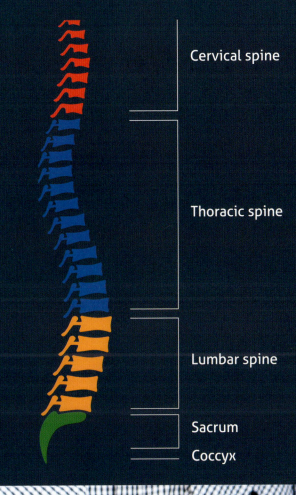

Cervical spine

Thoracic spine

Lumbar spine

Sacrum

Coccyx

The joints are prone to injury because they are in the less protected places of the body and are subject to great stresses.

JOINTS

The skeletons of animals would be too stiff to move or would fall in a disorderly heap if they were not carefully fitted with joints. A joint is a connection that holds together two or more bones or other hard structures. Joints have two main purposes: They give support, and they allow movement where it is needed.

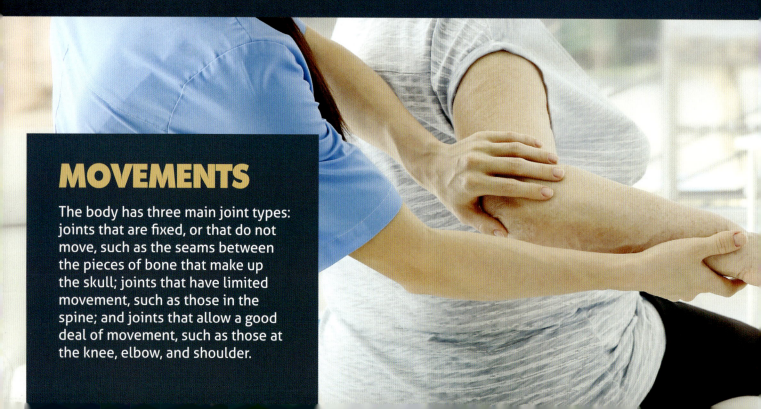

MOVEMENTS

The body has three main joint types: joints that are fixed, or that do not move, such as the seams between the pieces of bone that make up the skull; joints that have limited movement, such as those in the spine; and joints that allow a good deal of movement, such as those at the knee, elbow, and shoulder.

EASING MOVEMENT

In order to ease movement, a layer of cartilage covers the ends of the bones of many moveable joints and there is fluid in the space between them. Moveable joints are held together by bands of connective tissue called ligaments.

WHAT IS CARTILAGE?

Cartilage is a more flexible material than bone. It serves as a protective, cushioning layer where bones come together. It also connects the ribs to the breastbone and provides a structural base for the nose and the external ear. An infant's skeleton is made of cartilage that is gradually replaced by bone as the infant grows into an adult.

Cartilage as seen under a microscope.

Cartilage on each side of the nose bone gives the nose its shape.

THE MUSCULAR SYSTEM

All animal movement depends on the use of muscles. Whether the movement is as simple as opening the eyes or as complex as running the high hurdles at a track event, each is the result of a complex series of electric, chemical, and physical interactions involving the brain, the central nervous system, and the muscles themselves.

MUSCLES AND TENDONS

The muscular system consists of the muscles and associated tendons. The latter are fibrous bands of connective tissue that attach striated (skeletal) muscles to bone.

WHAT DOES THE MUSCULAR SYSTEM DO?

The primary task of the muscular system is to aid in movement. However, movement is just one of the functions of muscle. Muscle plays a key role in metabolism and thermoregulation. Muscles help move food through the intestine and urine out of the bladder. Without muscle, the heart could not pump blood through the body.

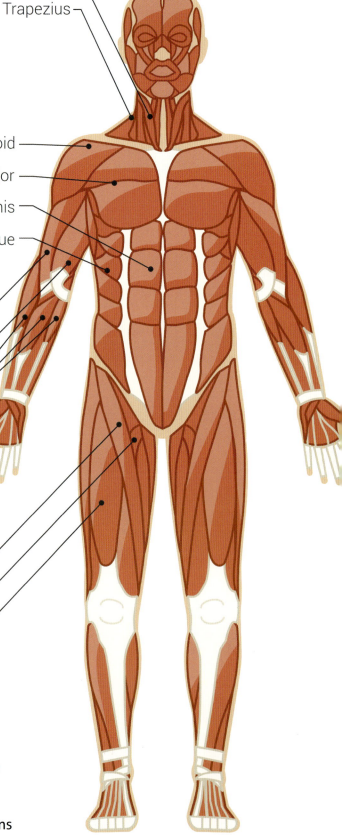

Sternocleidomastoid

Trapezius

Deltoid

Pectoralis Major

Rectus abdominis

External Oblique

Triceps brachii

Biceps brachii

Finger flexors

Sartorius

Adductor longus

Rectus femoris

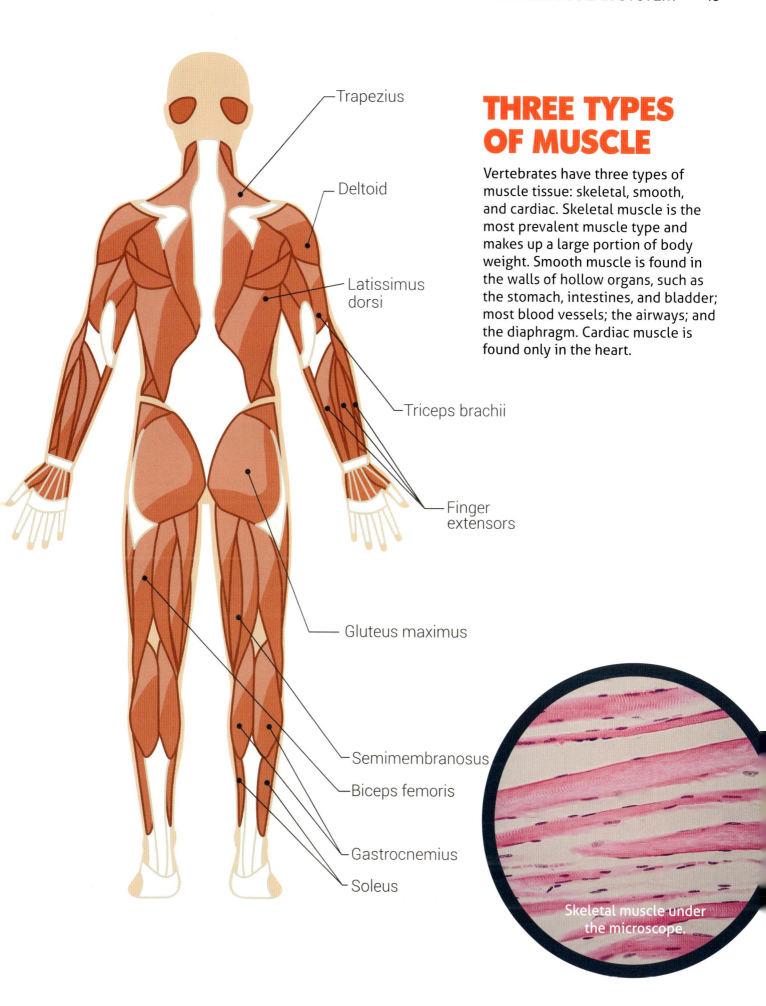

Trapezius

Deltoid

Latissimus dorsi

Triceps brachii

Finger extensors

Gluteus maximus

Semimembranosus

Biceps femoris

Gastrocnemius

Soleus

THREE TYPES OF MUSCLE

Vertebrates have three types of muscle tissue: skeletal, smooth, and cardiac. Skeletal muscle is the most prevalent muscle type and makes up a large portion of body weight. Smooth muscle is found in the walls of hollow organs, such as the stomach, intestines, and bladder; most blood vessels; the airways; and the diaphragm. Cardiac muscle is found only in the heart.

Skeletal muscle under the microscope.

SKELETAL MUSCLE

Skeletal muscle lies under the skin. It is made up of long threads, or fibers. Skeletal muscle controls movement, posture (position of the body), and balance. A person can move skeletal muscle just by thinking about it and then doing it.

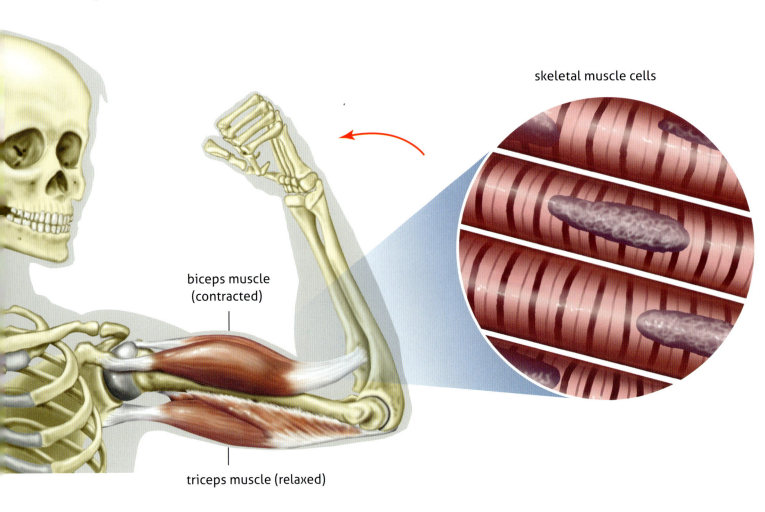

skeletal muscle cells

biceps muscle (contracted)

triceps muscle (relaxed)

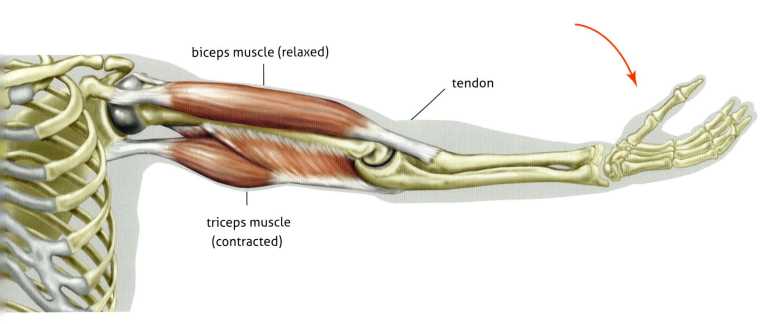

biceps muscle (relaxed)

tendon

triceps muscle (contracted)

FOUR FAST FACTS

1 Cordlike structures called tendons connect skeletal muscle to the skeleton.

2 As skeletal muscle tightens, or contracts, it gets shorter. It pulls on the bones attached to it. As the muscle relaxes, it gets longer. It lets the bones fall back into place. In this way skeletal muscle makes the bones move the parts of the body.

3 To make skeletal muscle move, the brain sends a message along a type of nerve called a motor nerve. Motor nerves end in the fibers of the muscle. There the nerves release chemicals that start a wave of electrical and chemical activity. This activity creates energy that moves the muscle.

4 Some of the energy also goes into the body as heat. This means that muscle movement helps to keep the body at the right temperature.

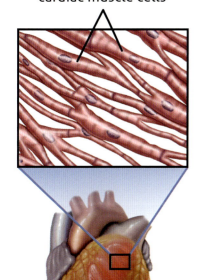

cardiac muscle cells

heart

CARDIAC MUSCLE

Cardiac muscle is located in the heart. The fibers of this muscle form a structure like a net. The fibers form the chambers, or hollow areas, of the heart. As the cardiac muscle contracts and relaxes, blood moves in and out of the chambers.

Cardiac muscle is involuntary muscle, which means that it moves automatically. A person does not have to think about telling the heart to beat. The cardiac muscle does not have nerves to tell it to move, either. A special strip of cardiac muscle releases bursts of electricity that help the heart to beat in a regular rhythm.

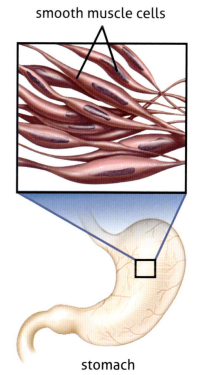

smooth muscle cells

stomach

SMOOTH MUSCLE

Smooth muscle helps to move food through the digestive system. It lines the intestines and the stomach. Smooth muscle also moves the diaphragm, which helps with breathing. Smooth muscle makes blood vessels tighten and relax, too. Like cardiac muscle, smooth muscle is involuntary muscle. The nervous system and body chemicals control the actions of smooth muscle.

THE CIRCULATORY SYSTEM

All animals need to move important fluids through their body. The fluids move through what is called a circulatory system. The fluids carry nutrients and gases, like oxygen, that keep the animals alive. The fluids also remove wastes from the body. In humans and some other animals they also carry substances that help the body fight infection. The circulatory system of humans consists of two parts: the cardiovascular system and the lymphatic system.

THE CARDIOVASCULAR SYSTEM

The main fluid in humans and most other animals is blood. It is transported through the cardiovascular system. This system consists of the heart and a network of blood vessels.

A technician draws blood.

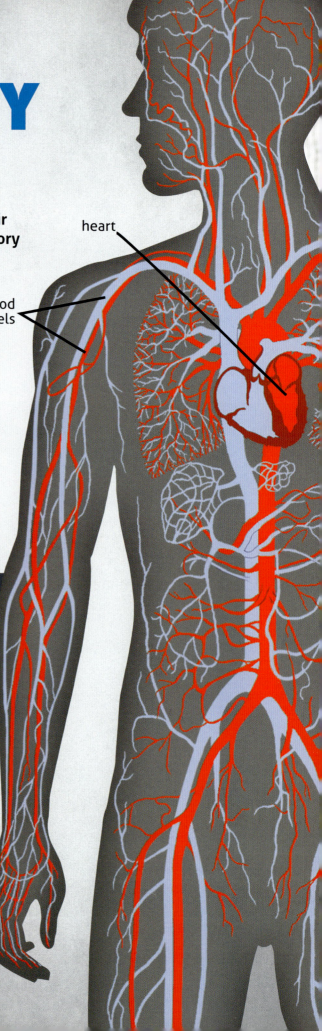

heart

blood vessels

THE HEART

The heart is a muscle that is divided into two nearly identical halves: one half receives blood from the lungs and sends it to the rest of the body, the other half sends blood that has traveled through the body back to the lungs. When the heart muscle contracts, the blood is forced out into arteries and enters small capillaries. Blood returns to the heart through veins.

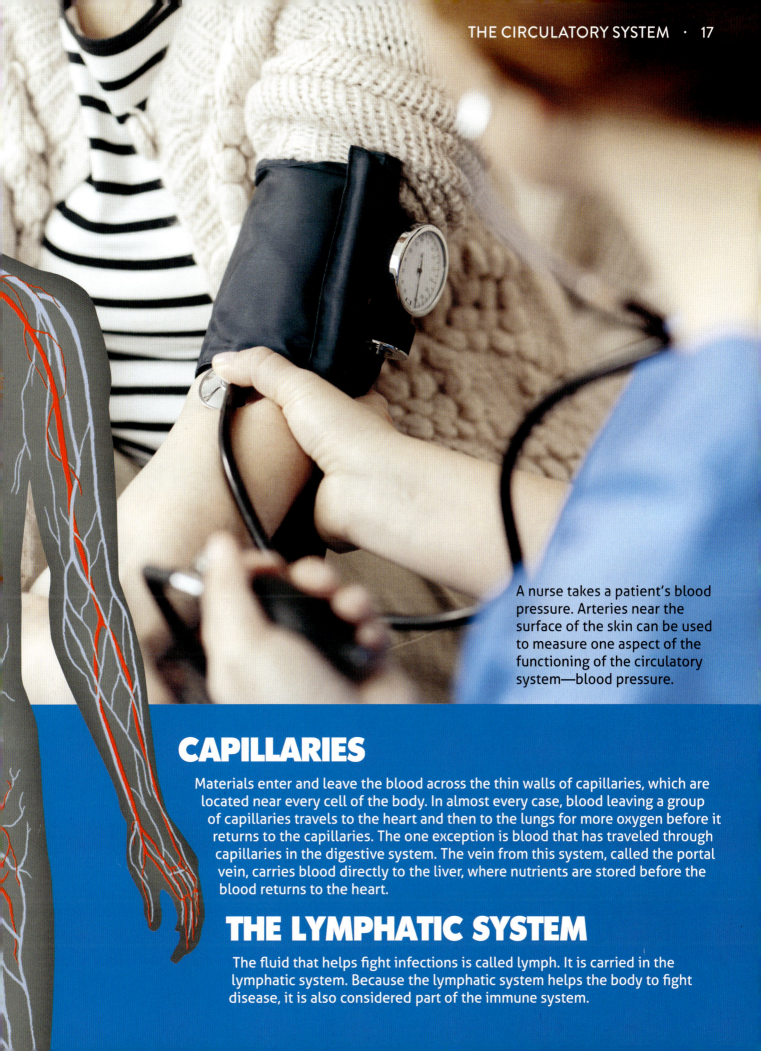

A nurse takes a patient's blood pressure. Arteries near the surface of the skin can be used to measure one aspect of the functioning of the circulatory system—blood pressure.

CAPILLARIES

Materials enter and leave the blood across the thin walls of capillaries, which are located near every cell of the body. In almost every case, blood leaving a group of capillaries travels to the heart and then to the lungs for more oxygen before it returns to the capillaries. The one exception is blood that has traveled through capillaries in the digestive system. The vein from this system, called the portal vein, carries blood directly to the liver, where nutrients are stored before the blood returns to the heart.

THE LYMPHATIC SYSTEM

The fluid that helps fight infections is called lymph. It is carried in the lymphatic system. Because the lymphatic system helps the body to fight disease, it is also considered part of the immune system.

THE
HEART

A muscular, pear-shaped organ slightly larger than a clenched fist, the human heart is the center of the circulatory system.

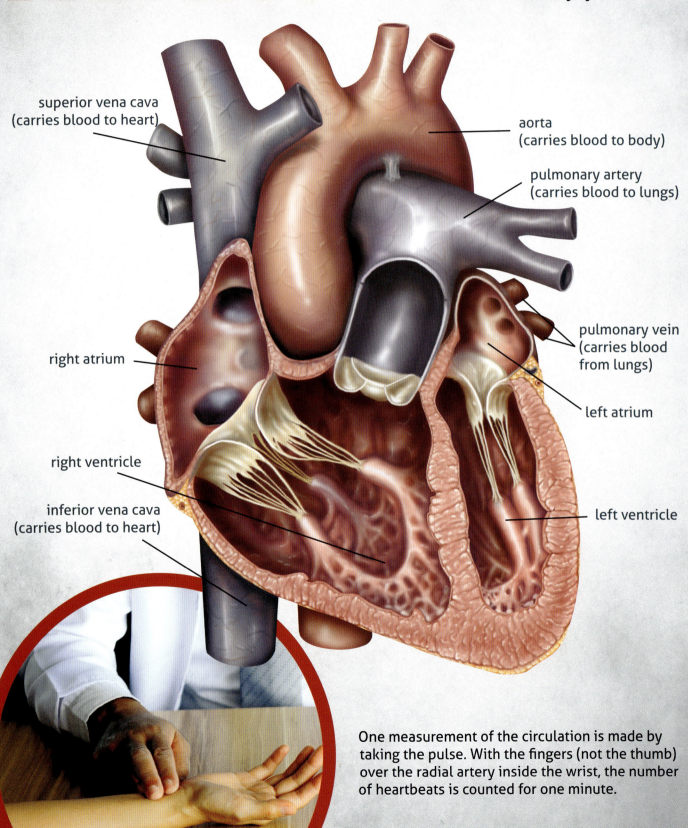

superior vena cava
(carries blood to heart)

aorta
(carries blood to body)

pulmonary artery
(carries blood to lungs)

right atrium

pulmonary vein
(carries blood
from lungs)

left atrium

right ventricle

inferior vena cava
(carries blood to heart)

left ventricle

One measurement of the circulation is made by taking the pulse. With the fingers (not the thumb) over the radial artery inside the wrist, the number of heartbeats is counted for one minute.

FIVE FAST FACTS

1 The human heart pumps blood through the body at a rate of more than about 4 quarts (3.8 liters) per minute.

2 The heart of an adult weighs between about 8 and 12 ounces (230 and 340 grams) and beats an average of 72 times per minute.

3 During a lifetime of 70 years, it will beat about 2.5 billion times and pump a total of 35 million gallons (132 million liters) or more of blood.

4 Small animals generally have rapid heartbeats. A canary's heart beats about 1,000 times per minute.

5 The heart rests only about 0.4 second between beats.

THE HEART'S STRUCTURE

The human heart is divided into right and left halves. Each half is divided into two hollow sections called chambers. The upper chambers are called atria. (Each of these chambers is called an atrium.) The lower chambers are called ventricles.

THE FLOW OF BLOOD

Blood from the body flows into the right atrium. This blood carries a waste product called carbon dioxide. The blood then passes into the right ventricle. The right ventricle pumps the blood to the lungs. In the lungs, blood picks up oxygen and releases carbon dioxide. The oxygen-rich blood enters the heart's left atrium. The blood then passes into the left ventricle. The left ventricle pumps the blood throughout the body.

CONTRACT AND RELAX

The action of the heart can be heard through a listening device, called a stethoscope, placed against the chest. The typical, healthy heart sound, "lub-dub…lub-dub," corresponds to the heart's contractions and relaxations. The low, dull "lub" sound is caused by the closing of the valves between the atria and ventricles. The shorter, higher-pitched "dub" sound is caused by the closing of the valves of the arteries leading out of the heart.

BLOOD

The life fluid of the body is blood. Blood flows to all parts of the body through the arteries, veins, and capillaries of the circulatory system. The walls of these vessels are made of living cells, through which nutrients and waste products pass to and from the blood. Blood also transports proteins and chemicals that help in fighting disease.

WHAT MAKES UP BLOOD?

Blood cells make up about half the volume of blood. These cells form inside bone marrow, which is a soft tissue inside bones. There are three main types of blood cell: red cells, white cells, and platelets. The watery part of the blood is the plasma. Most of the plasma is water. Plasma also contains nutrients, chemicals, hormones, and wastes.

Red blood cells under a microscope.

RED BLOOD CELLS

Red blood cells are the most numerous kind of blood cell. Their main job is to transport oxygen. In each cell, an iron-rich substance called hemoglobin carries the oxygen. Hemoglobin and oxygen together give blood its red color.

White blood cells under a microscope.

WHITE BLOOD CELLS

White blood cells, or leukocytes, help to keep the body healthy. Some swallow up tiny living things called bacteria or other foreign substances. Others release proteins that attack invading substances. Still others help to break down and remove dead cells. There are far fewer white cells, or leukocytes, than there are red cells. In a healthy adult there is approximately one white cell for every 650–700 red cells.

Blood and plasma being donated.

Platelets clumping.

PLATELETS

Platelets are the smallest of the blood cells. They are able to stick to one another and form blood clots. Clots plug holes that may develop in the walls of blood vessels. This helps stop bleeding.

THE RESPIRATORY SYSTEM

The respiratory system helps in gas exchange by taking in oxygen from the air and expelling carbon dioxide from the body. Air enters the nose and mouth and travels through the larynx, or voice box, and trachea, or windpipe. At the lungs, the trachea branches to form two bronchi (singular, bronchus); each bronchus enters one of the lungs. In the lungs the bronchi branch further, forming smaller airways called bronchioles, which further divide many times to form a very large number of small air spaces called alveoli.

FIVE FAST FACTS

1 The average adult normally takes about 16 breaths per minute when awake and about six to eight per minute when asleep.

2 Newborn babies breathe up to 44 times a minute.

3 Although the total air capacity in a person's lungs is roughly 300 cubic inches (4,916 cubic centimeters), the volume of air in a normal breath averages only about 30 cubic inches (492 cubic centimeters).

4 The lungs never empty completely. Even after the most vigorous expiration, they still contain about 60 cubic inches (983 cubic centimeters) of air.

5 There are more than 600 million alveoli in the average person's lungs.

THE BREATHING CYCLE

The brain controls breathing. It tells the diaphragm, a muscle at the base of the lungs, to move up and down. The brain also tells the muscles between the ribs to move in and out.

When the diaphragm moves down and the ribs move out, the area inside the chest grows larger. Air then flows into the lungs and makes them expand. Blood in the capillaries picks up oxygen from the air in the alveoli. The blood then brings the oxygen through the cardiovascular system to all parts of the body.

As the blood picks up oxygen, it also brings carbon dioxide from the body to the alveoli. The rib muscles and the diaphragm then relax. As the area inside the chest shrinks, the lungs decrease in size. The smaller size forces out air, including the carbon dioxide.

Alveoli

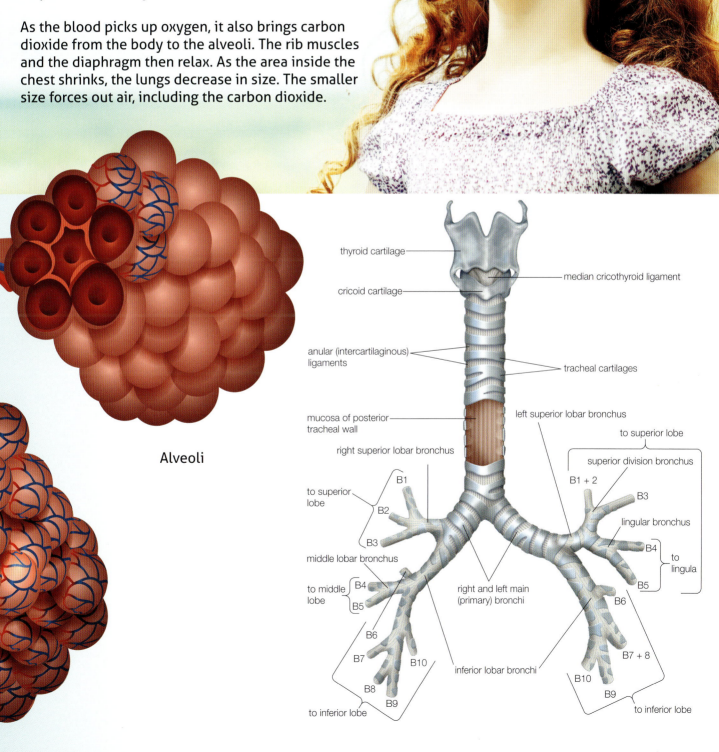

thyroid cartilage

median cricothyroid ligament

cricoid cartilage

anular (intercartilaginous) ligaments

tracheal cartilages

mucosa of posterior tracheal wall

left superior lobar bronchus

to superior lobe

right superior lobar bronchus

superior division bronchus

B1 + 2

B3

B1

lingular bronchus

to superior lobe

B2

B4

B3

to lingula

middle lobar bronchus

B5

to middle lobe

B4

B5

right and left main (primary) bronchi

B6

B6

B7 + 8

B7

B10

B10

inferior lobar bronchi

B8

B9

B9

to inferior lobe

to inferior lobe

COLD, FLU, AND ASTHMA

The respiratory system is subject to a wide variety of ailments. The most frequent attacks come from common cold and flu viruses. The lungs are especially vulnerable to allergic diseases such as asthma.

COLDS

The cold is one of the most common illnesses to affect humans. In fact, children may get 6 to 10 colds a year. People often catch colds during cold weather, but chilly temperatures are not the cause. Viruses, or tiny germs that enter the body, cause colds. More than 200 different viruses can cause a cold. Cold viruses spread easily from person to person. Coughing and sneezing force a cold virus into the air. People may then breathe in the virus. They may also pick up a virus by touching surfaces where viruses have landed. Then when they touch their noses, the virus enters the body.

INFLUENZA

A viral infection of the respiratory passages known as influenza, or flu, may be accompanied by symptoms of fever, chills, headache, muscle ache, sore throat, and weakness. It is spread by breathing airborne droplets infected with one of three influenza viruses—A, B, or C. The incubation period is two to three days. In general, type A is more debilitating than type B, and type B more than type C. Since type C causes only minor illness, it is sometimes mistaken for a common cold.

A woman receives a vaccine against influenza.

ASTHMA

Asthma is a respiratory disorder marked by sudden episodes of coughing, wheezing, shortness of breath, and feelings of suffocation. Asthma causes the muscles surrounding the bronchioles to constrict so much that air has difficulty reaching the lungs. The mucous membranes in the affected parts of the lungs swell, contributing to the problem by making the passageways even narrower and producing thick mucus. The person suffering an asthma episode, or attack as it is often called, then experiences difficulty in breathing. The presence of mucus in the lungs causes a further feeling of suffocation.

A girl uses an inhaler to help her asthma symptoms.

THE DIGESTIVE SYSTEM

What happens to food after it is eaten? The body uses various kinds of food for energy and growth. To be used, however, food must be converted into nutrients that can be carried through the bloodstream and absorbed by the organism's cells. This conversion process is called digestion.

WHAT MAKES UP THE DIGESTIVE SYSTEM?

The digestive system consists of a series of connected organs that work together to break down, or digest, food into small molecules that are absorbed into the circulatory system, which then carries them to the body's tissues. The major structures of the digestive system are the mouth, tongue, esophagus, stomach, intestines, rectum, and anus. The liver, gallbladder, and pancreas also are part of the system.

HOW DIGESTION STARTS

The digestion of food is both a mechanical and a chemical process. Food enters through the mouth, where chewing and saliva start to break it up and make it easier to swallow. Next, the food travels down through the esophagus to the stomach. Contractions of the stomach's muscular wall continue to break down the food mechanically, and chemical digestion continues when acid and enzymes are secreted into the stomach cavity.

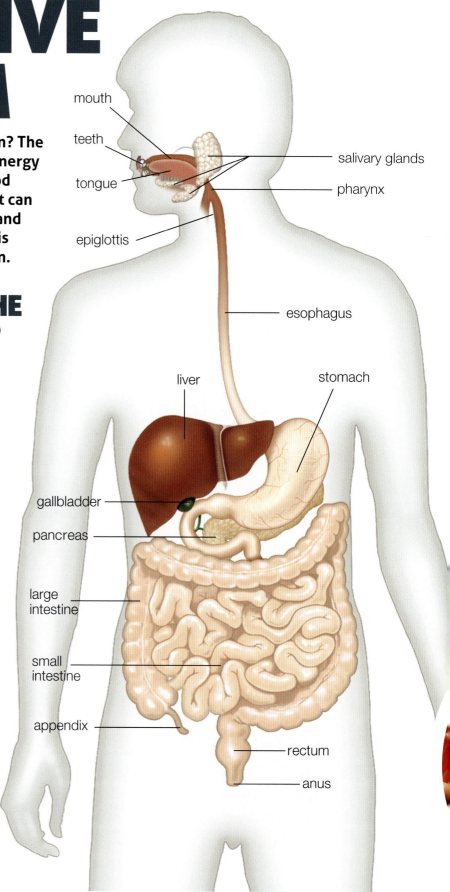

mouth

teeth

tongue

epiglottis

salivary glands

pharynx

esophagus

liver

stomach

gallbladder

pancreas

large intestine

small intestine

appendix

rectum

anus

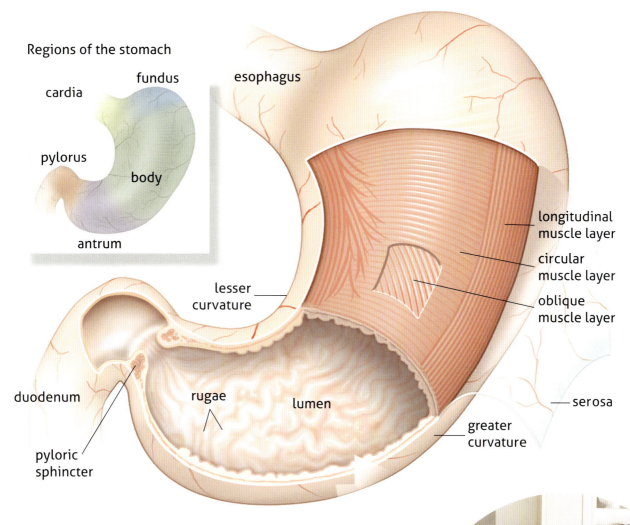

Regions of the stomach

cardia
fundus
esophagus
pylorus
body
antrum

longitudinal muscle layer
circular muscle layer
oblique muscle layer

lesser curvature

serosa

duodenum
rugae
lumen
greater curvature

pyloric sphincter

From the time a meal is eaten, it takes from 30 to 40 hours for food to travel the length of the digestive tract.

IN THE INTESTINES

From the stomach, liquefied food gradually passes into the small intestine. In the first part of the small intestine, called the duodenum, enzymes from the pancreas are added. These enzymes complete the chemical breakdown of the food. The digestion of fat is aided by bile, which is made in the liver and stored in the gall bladder. The small intestine of an adult is about 21 feet (6.4 meters) long. Most of its length is devoted to absorbing the nutrients released during these digestive activities.

The liquid remainder of the food enters the large intestine, or colon, which is about 6 feet (1.8 meters) long. It is more than twice as wide as the small intestine. In the large intestine most of the fluid from the digested food is reabsorbed into the blood. The relatively dry residues are expelled through the anus as feces.

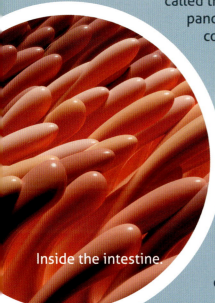

Inside the intestine.

THE URINARY SYSTEM

The various activities of the body create waste by-products that must be expelled in order to maintain health. To excrete certain fluid wastes, the body has a specialized filtering and recycling system known as the urinary, or excretory, system. Solid wastes are eliminated, or egested, through the large intestine.

THE ORGANS OF THE URINARY SYSTEM

The kidneys, ureters, bladder, and urethra are the main organs of the urinary, or excretory, system. These structures work together to maintain normal levels of water and of certain small molecules such as sodium and potassium in the body.

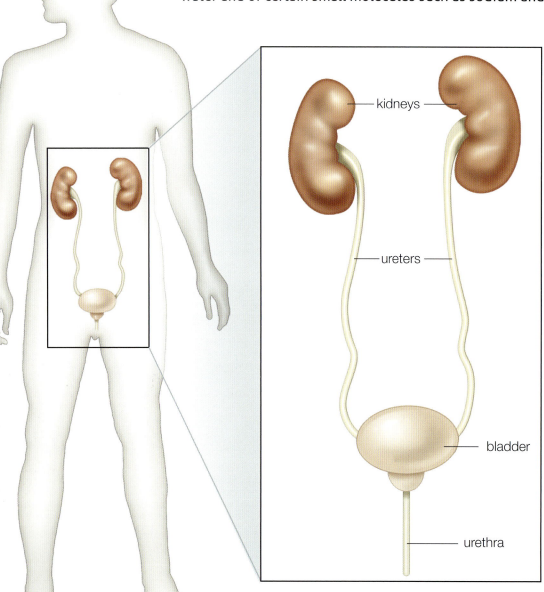

kidneys

ureters

bladder

urethra

HOW IT WORKS

The kidneys function as selective filters. As blood passes through the kidneys, the organs remove certain molecules that are in excess supply in the blood and conserve those molecules that are in short supply. The fluid that leaves the kidneys, known as urine, travels through the ureters to the sac-like bladder. The bladder holds the urine until it is voided from the body through the urethra.

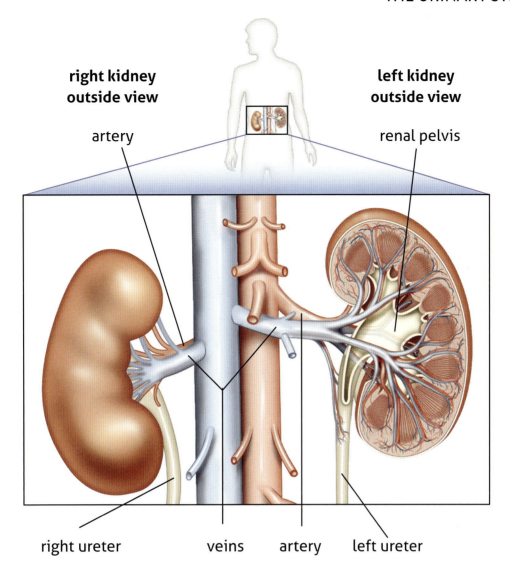

right kidney outside view

left kidney outside view

artery

renal pelvis

right ureter   veins   artery   left ureter

FIVE FAST FACTS

1 The bladder is a muscular organ at the bottom of the abdomen that expands like a sack as it fills.

2 The bladder of an adult can hold about ⅓ quart (350 milliliters) of urine.

3 When the bladder is full, nerve endings in the bladder send a message to the brain. This message lets the person know that the bladder needs to be emptied.

4 Each kidney is about 4 to 5 inches (10 to 12.5 centimeters) long.

5 If the kidneys fail, doctors may use a technique called dialysis to remove wastes from the blood. In dialysis the patient's blood travels out of the body, through a cleaning machine, and back into the body. Doctors may also transplant a healthy person's kidney into the patient.

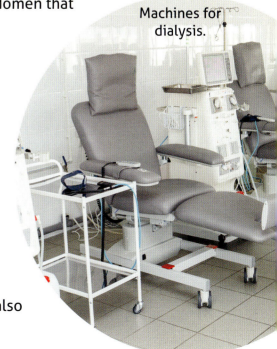

Machines for dialysis.

THE ENDOCRINE SYSTEM

The endocrine system is a body system in animals. It controls and regulates body processes by means of chemical messengers called hormones. The system is composed of a group of ductless glands located throughout the body that produce hormones in response to the body's needs. Once released, hormones may act on nearby structures, or they may travel in the blood to distant target organs.

HOMEOSTASIS

The task of the endocrine system is to maintain homeostasis, or balance, in the body. Because hormones have a powerful effect on the body, the production and release of these messengers is tightly regulated. Too much or too little of any hormone may cause the body to function improperly; in some cases this may result in disease or even death.

HOW MANY HORMONES?

The human body makes more than 20 major hormones. Growth hormone helps to build muscles. Epinephrine, also called adrenaline, makes the heart beat fast during stressful times. Insulin controls the level of sugar in the blood. Estrogen controls sexual development in females. Sexual development in males is controlled by testosterone.

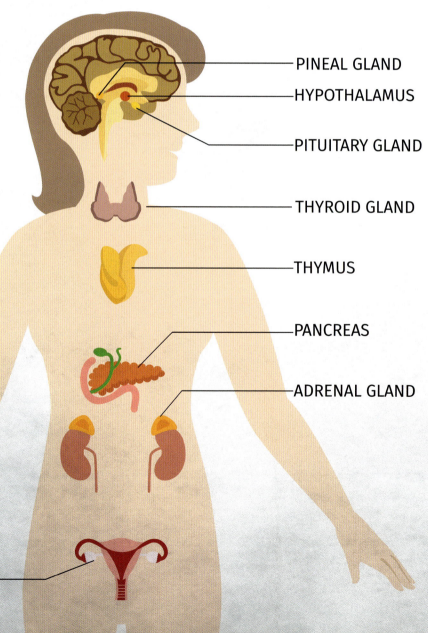

PINEAL GLAND

HYPOTHALAMUS

PITUITARY GLAND

THYROID GLAND

THYMUS

PANCREAS

ADRENAL GLAND

OVARIES (FEMALE)

THE MASTER GLAND

A key endocrine gland is the pituitary, which is located under the brain in the middle of the head. It produces at least eight hormones, which affect growth, kidney function, and development of some organs. Because some of the pituitary's hormones stimulate other glands to produce their own hormones, the pituitary is called the master gland.

OTHER GLANDS

The thyroid gland is located between the collar bones. The hormone produced by the thyroid controls the rate of the body's metabolism. Located on top of each kidney is an adrenal gland, which produces cortisone and epinephrine. The pancreas produces insulin and glucagon, the hormones that control the body's use of sugar and starches.

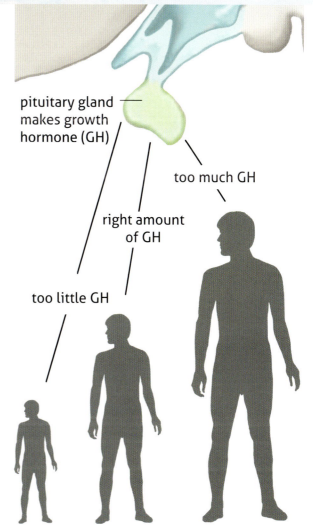

pituitary gland makes growth hormone (GH)

too much GH

right amount of GH

too little GH

THE NERVOUS SYSTEM

Information about the outside world as well as the inner workings of the human body speeds to and from the brain and spinal cord through nerves. Nerves are bundles of the long, tubelike extensions of nerve cells. Impulses fired through them uniquely convey information throughout the body.

PERIPHERAL AND CENTRAL

The nervous system in humans has two main parts: the central nervous system and the peripheral nervous system. The central nervous system consists of the brain and spinal cord. The peripheral nervous system consists of the nerves, which relay impulses between the central nervous system and the rest of the body. They transmit information by electrochemical means. The peripheral nervous system includes the autonomic nervous system, which controls and regulates the internal organs without any conscious recognition or effort by the individual.

DIFFERENT NERVES, DIFFERENT FUNCTIONS

Sensory nerves carry information from the sense organs and other body receptors to the central nervous system for processing. Then motor nerves carry the processed information from the central nervous system to the glands and muscles for appropriate action. The nervous system also includes mixed nerves, which have separate sensory nerve fibers and motor nerve fibers.

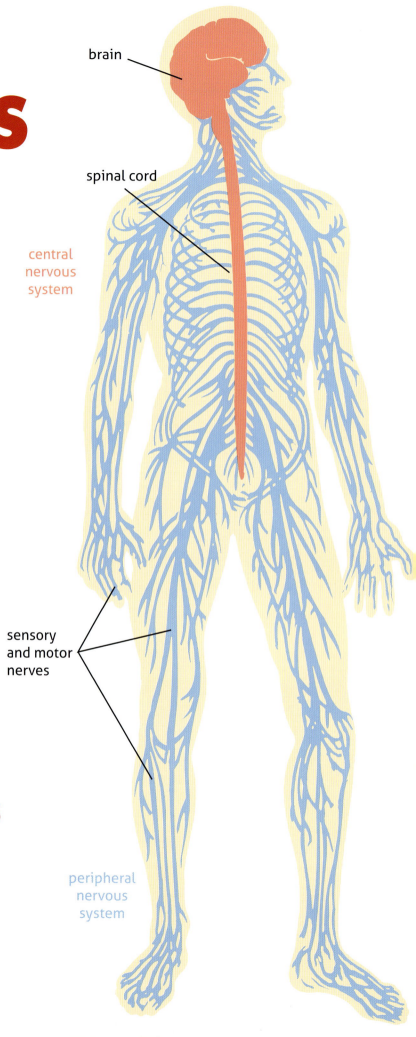

brain

spinal cord

central nervous system

sensory and motor nerves

peripheral nervous system

NEURONS

Nearly all neurons, or nerve cells, have the same general structure. They usually have a round or pyramid-shaped cell body, which contains the nucleus and other basic cell parts. "Trees" of branching fibers called dendrites sprout from the cell body. In general, the dendrites receive nerve impulses and conduct them toward the cell body. Also extending from the cell body is a long tubelike fiber called an axon. The axon generally transmits nerve impulses away from the cell body to other cells.

SYNAPSES

A neuron connects with others at junctions called synapses. Typically, the axon of one neuron forms a synapse with the dendrite of another neuron.

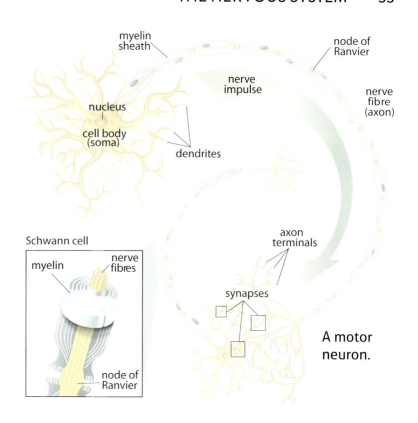

A motor neuron.

Sensory nerves relay information about hot and cold.

THE
BRAIN

The human brain is a miraculous organ. It regulates thought, memory, judgment, personal identity, and other aspects of what is commonly called mind. It also regulates aspects of the body—including body temperature, blood pressure, and the activity of internal organs—to help the body respond to its environment and to maintain the body's health.

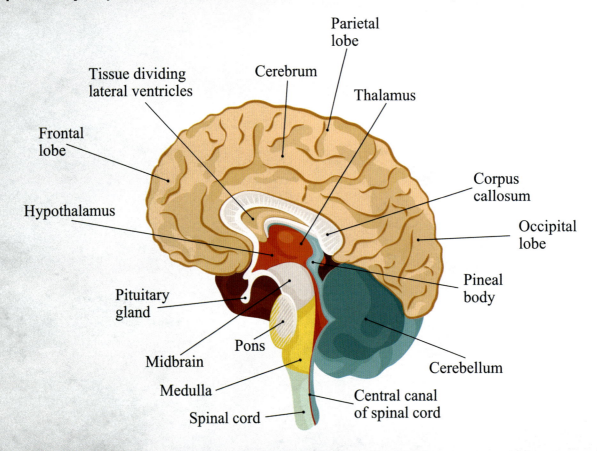

FOUR FAST FACTS

1. The brain receives the oxygen and food it needs to function by way of a vast network of arteries that carries fresh blood to every part of the brain.

2. The brain of a human adult weighs about 3 pounds (1.4 kilograms).

3. The medulla, at the base of the brain stem, transmits all signals between the spinal cord and the higher parts of the brain and also governs mechanisms essential to life: heartbeat, blood pressure, and breathing.

4. The brain is composed of two principal types of cells—neurons and glial cells (also called neuroglia). The neurons perform the essential tasks of the brain, and the glial cells provide a kind of protective environment for the neurons.

PARTS OF THE BRAIN

The brain looks rather like a mushroom contained within the skull. The cap of the mushroom—the very top of the brain—is the cerebrum, and the stem of the mushroom—the part of the brain attached to the spinal cord—is the brain stem. At the back of the head, lying between the brain stem and the cerebrum, is the cerebellum.

An illustration representing neurons in the brain.

You are using your brain when you are reading a book and when you are riding a bike.

FROM BASIC TO ADVANCED

The brain stem, the lowest part of the brain, is involved with the most basic processes, such as relaying information between parts of the brain or between the brain and the body and regulating basic body functions. The cerebellum, behind it, controls balance and coordination. The cerebrum, the topmost part of the brain, is the "thinking" part of the brain.

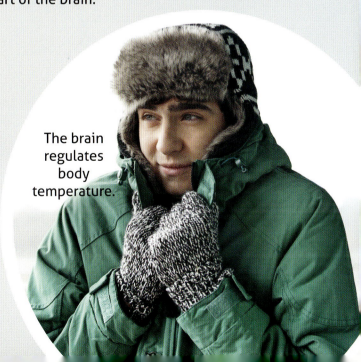

The brain regulates body temperature.

MEMORY

The mental storing and recalling of information, called memory, is essential for intelligent behavior. Without memory, learning would be impossible. Exactly how the memory works is not fully understood, but it is known that memory storage requires a chemical change in any number of the brain's more than 10 billion neurons. Memories are formed by chemical changes between the neurons of certain parts of the brain associated with memory—the cerebral cortex, thalamus, and hippocampus. Every time a person learns something new, chemical changes cause new pathways, or memory traces, to develop between neurons. These memory traces can be activated at any time to reproduce the thoughts called memories.

Motor-skill memory in action.

MOTOR-SKILL MEMORY

There are two distinct types of memory: motor-skill memory and factual memory. The ability to memorize motor skills, such as walking or riding a bicycle, makes it possible to perform many routine functions without a great deal of conscious thought. Within five to six hours of learning a new motor skill, the ability to perform the task becomes stored permanently in a person's brain. If the storage process is interrupted during this time by learning another physical skill, however, the first lesson may be erased.

FACTUAL MEMORY

Factual memory enables a person to remember things of varying complexity. Telephone numbers, the story line of a book, the face of a distant relative, and a summer afternoon are all retained through factual memory.

LEVELS OF MEMORY

There are three levels of memory. Immediate memory is the ability to retain information long enough to perform tasks and maintain a train of thought. Short-term memory is the ability to retain and recall data for more than a few minutes and may function as a way station between new information and long-term memory. Long-term memory makes it possible to store information for a few months or as long as a lifetime. Many researchers believe that memory functions best when new information is associated with existing memories. Data that are nonsensical or irrelevant tend to be lost.

Although it may appear undesirable, forgetting actually serves several important functions. It allows people to discard data that are no longer useful, and it allows them to orient themselves to the present.

Practice, or repetition, is the method by which most new information is learned. Generally, information that is learned over an extended period of time is better remembered.

THE INTEGUMENTARY SYSTEM

The integumentary system comprises a network of features that forms the covering of an organism. In humans, the main structure of the system is the skin, or integument. Hair, nails, and a variety of glands also are part of the integumentary system.

THE LARGEST ORGAN

The largest of the body's organs, the skin forms a barrier that protects the inner structures of the body. It keeps out foreign substances and prevents excessive water evaporation. The nerves in the skin provide sensory information about the environment that is conveyed to the brain through sensory nerves. The skin also helps keep the body's temperature close to 98.6 °F (about 37 °C): heat is conserved by reducing blood flow through the skin or is expended by increasing blood flow and by evaporation of sweat from the skin.

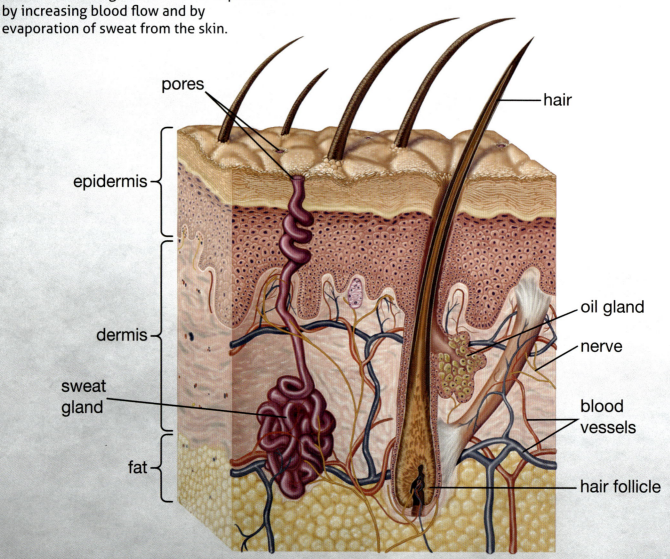

pores

hair

epidermis

dermis

oil gland

nerve

sweat gland

blood vessels

fat

hair follicle

FIVE FAST FACTS

(1) Skin is composed of three layers: epidermis, dermis, and subcutaneous fatty tissue.

(2) The outer layer, the epidermis, is constantly flaking off and being renewed from the dermis. The epidermis itself has four layers.

(3) The dermis is composed of elastic collagen fibers, blood vessels, nerves, lymph vessels, hair follicles, and sweat glands. Nerve endings are contained in the papillae, tiny projections that fit the dermis to the epidermis like parts of a puzzle.

(4) Papillae are especially prominent on the palms of the hands and soles of the feet, where the epidermis is ridged and furrowed in patterns of tiny whorls and loops. These patterns are what form each person's unique set of fingerprints and footprints.

(5) Subcutaneous fatty tissue is the deepest layer of the skin. It is composed of connective tissue, blood vessels, and fat cells. This layer binds the skin to underlying structures, insulates the body from cold, and stores energy in the form of fat.

HAIR AND NAILS

Nails, like the claws, hoofs, and horns of animals, are merely thickened and hardened epidermis.

PREGNANCY AND BIRTH

All living things reproduce, or create offspring. Animals' offspring are often called babies. The body parts that allow animals to create babies belong to the reproductive system. Some animals can create offspring through asexual reproduction. This means that one animal creates offspring on its own. Most animals, including humans, use sexual reproduction to have babies. This means that two sex cells, one from a male and one from a female, join together to create a baby.

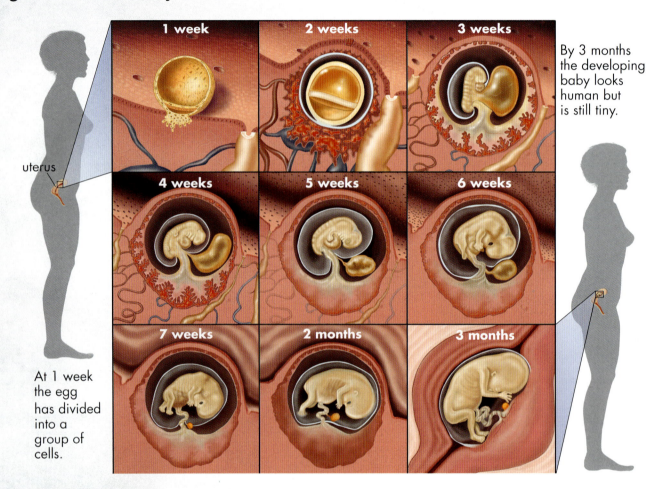

uterus

1 week

2 weeks

3 weeks

By 3 months the developing baby looks human but is still tiny.

4 weeks

5 weeks

6 weeks

7 weeks

2 months

3 months

At 1 week the egg has divided into a group of cells.

PREGNANCY

Once an egg from the mother is fertilized by a sperm from the father, pregnancy (or gestation) begins. The fertilized egg moves into the woman's uterus. As it travels it starts to divide into many more cells. After about five or six days these cells burrow into the wall of the uterus. There the cells begin to develop into a baby. At first the developing baby is called an embryo. After about eight weeks the baby is called a fetus.

THE AMNIOTIC SAC

In the uterus the baby grows inside a pouch called the amniotic sac. The amniotic sac is filled with clear liquid. The liquid protects the baby and lets it move around. A bundle of blood vessels, called the umbilical cord, connects the baby's belly to the placenta. The placenta is a structure that lines part of the uterus. The placenta brings nourishment from the mother's body to the baby. It also takes away wastes from the baby.

BIRTH

After about nine months of development the baby is ready to leave the woman's body. The bottom end of the uterus, called the cervix, expands to create a wide opening into the vagina, or birth canal. The muscles of the uterus contract to push the baby downward. The baby moves slowly through the vagina and out of the mother's body.

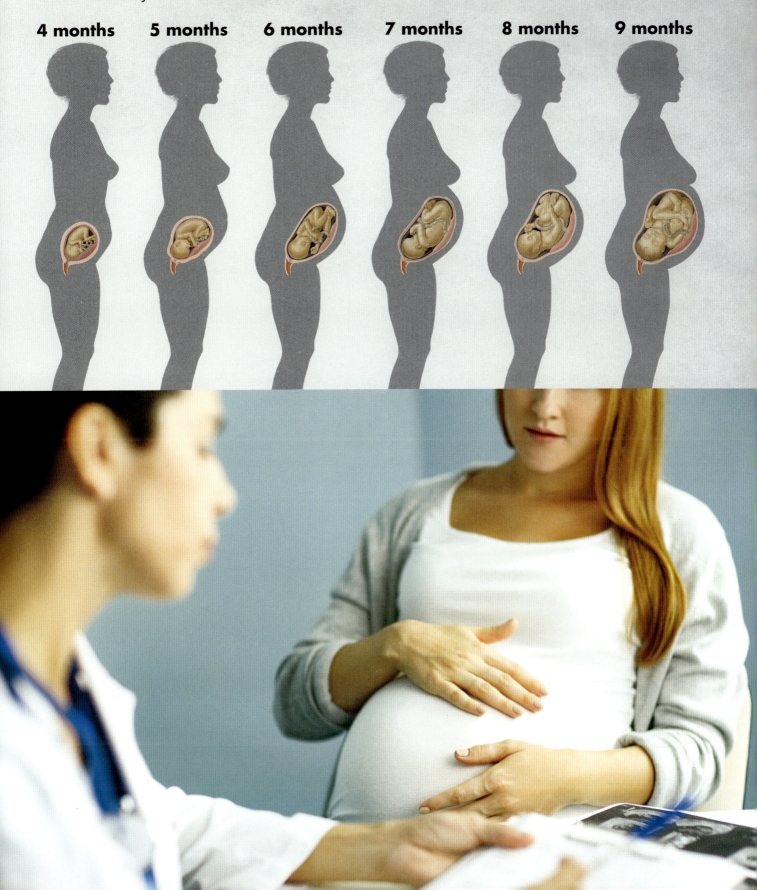

4 months   5 months   6 months   7 months   8 months   9 months

AGING

All living things, from their first moment of existence, begin the process of aging, or growing older. As children move toward adulthood, they become taller, stronger, and more independent. At some point in adulthood, however, a slow decline begins. The onset of aging happens at different times for different people. Most people start to feel some effects of aging in their 40s or 50s.

VISIBLE SIGNS OF AGING

In humans aging shows in many ways, some very visible: decline in height, shrinkage of muscle, thinning and graying of hair, and wrinkling of skin.

AGING AND CELLS

The effects of aging on internal parts of the body are especially significant. There is a progressive loss of cells in the brain, kidneys, and other vital organs. This cell loss has been ascribed to, among other things, errors in DNA replication, resulting in stoppage of a vital process. Whatever the reason, important tissues—ranging from the muscles to the brain—shrink and become less competent with age. Many of these changes are reflected in functional declines. Not only do nerve cells in the brain and the spinal cord diminish, but also those that remain conduct impulses at a slower rate so that the reaction time of the older animal is slowed. Memory often shows a decline.

HEARING

Another widespread decline is in the loss of cells involved in the hearing process. The loss is most marked for high pitches and may require the assistance of a battery-operated hearing aid.

STAYING ACTIVE

Disuse may be a significant factor in the impairment of memory and thinking just as it is in muscle weakness associated with aging. Disuse from an inactive physical life-style has been shown to accelerate the loss of bone, which results in the fractures so common in old age. Exercise slows this process and may even increase the bone mass. The increased susceptibility of the aged to pneumonia and influenza may be improved by vaccines. Progress in the medical area indicates that some of the declines produced by aging can be slowed.

THE IMMUNE SYSTEM

The immune system protects the body from substances called antigens. Some of the most harmful antigens are germs like viruses and bacteria, which cause illness. Parts of the immune system block antigens from entering the body. Other parts destroy the antigens that do enter.

The protection given by the immune system is called immunity. There are two basic types of immunity: natural and acquired.

NATURAL IMMUNITY

All animals, including humans, have natural immunity. It works against any antigen that enters or tries to enter the body. Skin is a part of natural immunity. It blocks many things from entering the body. Mucus in the nose also blocks antigens.

The immune system includes organs, vessels, and specialized cells and proteins. The main organs of the system are the thymus, lymph nodes, tonsils, spleen, and bone marrow. Several areas of the small intestine called Peyer's patches contain lymphoid tissue that produces specialized blood cells and other immune factors (proteins) that help fight infection. The vessels of the lymphatic system provide a link between the body's organs and specialized tissues of the immune system.

USE THE VR VIEWER TO SEE THE IMMUNE SYSTEM IN ACTION.

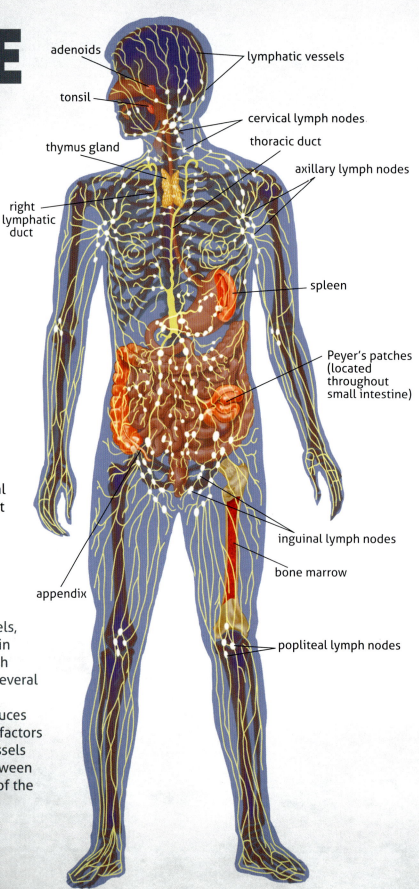

adenoids

lymphatic vessels

tonsil

cervical lymph nodes

thymus gland

thoracic duct

axillary lymph nodes

right lymphatic duct

spleen

Peyer's patches (located throughout small intestine)

inguinal lymph nodes

bone marrow

appendix

popliteal lymph nodes

ACQUIRED IMMUNITY

Only vertebrates—humans and other animals with backbones—have acquired immunity. With this kind of immunity, certain cells in the body can "remember" the types of antigens they have attacked in the past. This "memory" allows the acquired immune system to attack these antigens more strongly the next time they enter the body. Certain white blood cells, called lymphocytes, are important parts of the acquired immune system. Because of acquired immunity, people get certain diseases, like chicken pox, only once. Acquired immunity is also what makes vaccines work.

FAST FACTS

1 Lymph nodes are round or kidney-shaped organs usually found in groups distributed throughout the body, both close to the surface and deep.

2 A person has between 500 and 1,500 lymph nodes that range in size from very tiny to about 1 inch (2.5 centimeters) in diameter.

3 Lymph nodes consist of networks of fibers and cells. The cells may be motile, or able to move about, or fixed. The principal motile cells are the lymphocytes.

HEALTH AND DISEASE

A disease is a condition that impairs the proper function of the body or of one of its parts. All living things can succumb to disease.

DIAGNOSIS

Hundreds of different diseases exist in nature, and every disease has a cause, though the causes of some remain to be discovered. Each disease has a particular set of symptoms and signs—clues that assist in diagnosis. A symptom is something a patient can detect, such as nausea, bleeding, or pain. A sign is something that a doctor can observe in a patient, such as an abnormal heart rate.

INFECTIOUS DISEASES

Infectious diseases are diseases that are contagious. People may catch these diseases in a number of ways. Direct contact between humans spreads some infectious diseases. Other diseases are spread by certain animals, such as mosquitoes. Still other diseases spread through air, water, or food. Infectious diseases are caused by pathogens—disease-causing bacteria, viruses, fungi, and protozoa. Once a pathogen has entered the body, the person is said to be infected.

NONINFECTIOUS DISEASES

Many human diseases do not result from pathogens. These diseases are called noninfectious. They are not contagious. Some noninfectious diseases are inherited, or passed down through families. A person's lifestyle can lead to certain noninfectious diseases. People who eat poorly and do not exercise are in danger of getting heart disease or diabetes. People who smoke cigarettes are more likely to get lung cancer than nonsmokers.

STAYING HEALTHY

Some factors such as age and genetics that influence health cannot be controlled, but there are many practices and behaviors that enable people to maintain or improve their health. These include:

- getting proper nourishment
- exercising regularly
- getting adequate sleep
- maintaining cleanliness
- getting vaccinated
- managing stress
- getting regular medical and dental care

FIGHTING OFF INFECTION

FIRST LINE OF DEFENSE

As a first line of defense, a healthy body has a number of physical barriers against infection. The skin and mucous membranes covering the body and lining its cavities offer considerable resistance to invasion by infectious organisms. If these barriers are injured or burned, however, resistance drops.

SECOND LINE OF DEFENSE

When the first line of defense fails, the body calls up its second line of defense: the immune system. Circulating through the blood and lymph, white blood cells flock to infected areas and try to localize and suppress the infection. Some white blood cells, such as macrophages, engulf and digest the pathogens in a process known as phagocytosis.

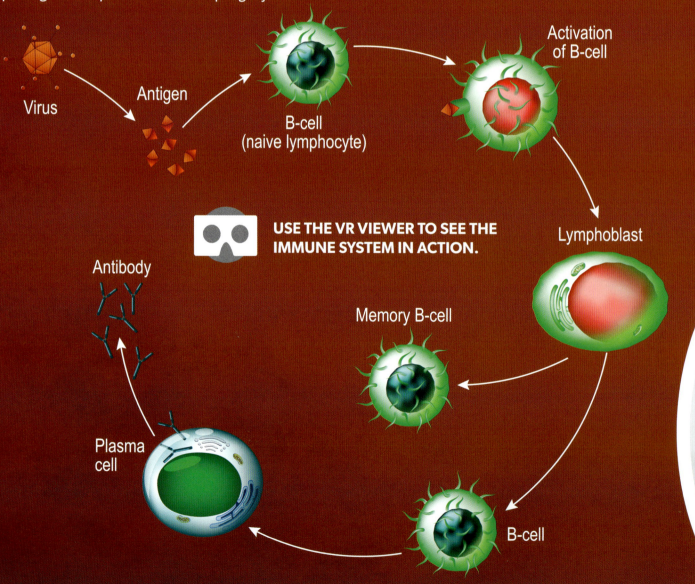

Virus

Antigen

B-cell
(naive lymphocyte)

Activation
of B-cell

Lymphoblast

USE THE VR VIEWER TO SEE THE IMMUNE SYSTEM IN ACTION.

Antibody

Memory B-cell

Plasma
cell

B-cell

LYMPHOCYTES

Lymphocytes, another group of white blood cells, play a key role during this line of defense. Lymphocytes are divided into two main classes, or types: T cells and B cells. T cells use several methods to kill pathogens directly, in some cases tagging them with markers so that other cells can attack them. B cells manufacture and release protective proteins called antibodies, which are "custom-designed" by the B cells to target specific pathogens. Some B cells remain in the body for years after the pathogen has been eliminated. This creates a biological "memory," giving the body a long-lasting immunity against future attacks by the same kind of invader.

DRUG THERAPY

Since the advent of antibiotic therapy in the 20th century, a broad range of infection-fighting drugs has been developed to work in conjunction with the body's immune system. The antibiotics penicillin and tetracycline, for instance, are very effective against some bacterial infections. However, antibiotics have no effect on infections caused by viruses, fungi, protozoa, or other parasites.

OUR SENSES

Sensory reception is the process by which a living organism is able to react to external or internal environmental changes. Information received through sensory receptors is interpreted by the central nervous system. When a receptor is stimulated, a message called a nerve impulse travels over a nerve fiber to the specific location in the brain where separate sensations, such as sight or hearing, are interpreted.

Vestibular sense in action.

RECEPTORS

Plants use sensory receptors to locate sources of light, to align themselves with gravity, and to time the processes of germination and flowering with changes in temperature and length of daylight. Animals depend on their senses to locate food, to avoid predators, and to monitor their environment. Highly acute senses can give an organism a decided survival advantage.

Chemoreceptors are used to smell.

MANY KINDS OF RECEPTORS

One way in which to classify sensory structures is by the stimuli to which they respond. For example, there are photoreceptors for light; mechanoreceptors for touch, sound, and equilibrium; thermoreceptors for heat; chemoreceptors for smell and taste; and nociceptors for painful stimuli.

HOW MANY SENSES ARE THERE?

Although the ancient philosopher Aristotle distinguished the five senses as sight, hearing, smell, taste, and touch, many more senses exist. Kinesthetic sense is the ability to feel motion through receptors found in muscles, tendons, and joints. Vestibular sense is the body's ability to balance itself, controlled by the body's inner ear. Skin itself senses not only pain and pressure but also cold and warmth.

The sense of touch in action.

OUR EYES

The human eye is a complex part of the body that is used for seeing. Eyes enable people to perform daily tasks and to learn about the world that surrounds them. Sight, or vision, is a rapidly occurring process that involves continuous interaction between the eye, the nervous system, and the brain. When someone looks at an object, what that person really sees is the light reflected from the object. This reflected light passes through the lens and falls on the retina of the eye. Here the light induces nerve impulses that travel through the optic nerve to the brain and then over other nerves to muscles and glands.

WHY DO WE BLINK?

Humans blink an average of once every six seconds. This washes the eye with a salty secretion from the tear, or lachrymal, glands. Each tear gland is about the size and shape of an almond. These glands are situated behind the upper eyelid at the outer corner of the eye. After passing over the eye, the liquid from the gland is drained into the nose through the tear duct at the inner corner of the eye.

PARTS OF THE EYE

The eye is made of three coats, or tunics. The outermost coat consists of the cornea and the sclera; the middle coat contains the main blood supply to the eye and consists of the choroid, the ciliary body, and the iris. The innermost layer is the retina.

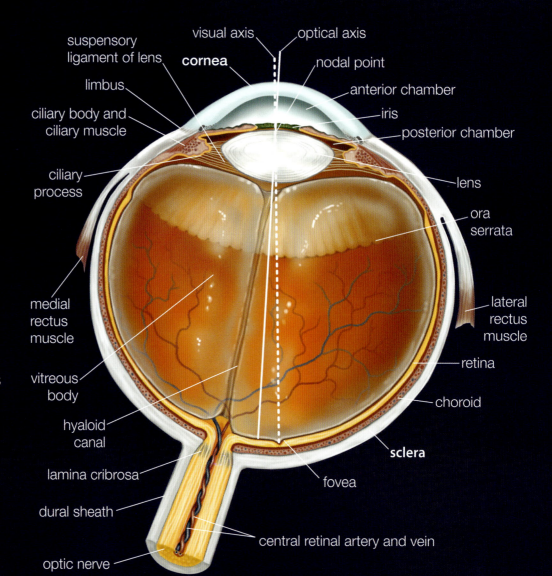

suspensory ligament of lens

visual axis

optical axis

cornea

nodal point

limbus

anterior chamber

ciliary body and ciliary muscle

iris

posterior chamber

ciliary process

lens

ora serrata

medial rectus muscle

lateral rectus muscle

vitreous body

retina

choroid

hyaloid canal

lamina cribrosa

sclera

dural sheath

fovea

central retinal artery and vein

optic nerve

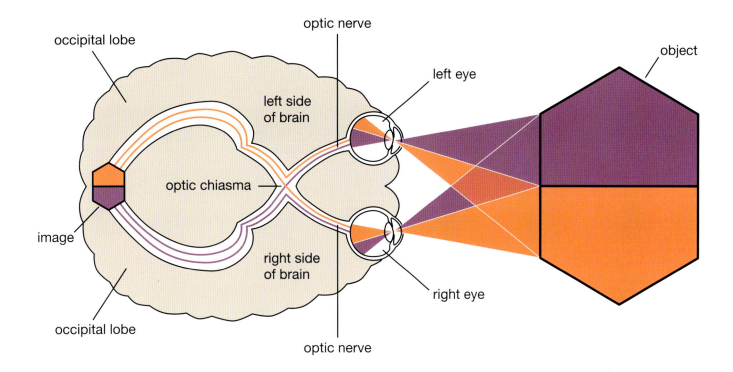

RODS AND CONES

The retina is a soft, transparent layer of nervous tissue made up of millions of light receptors. The retina is connected to the brain by the optic nerve. When light enters the eye it passes through the lens and focuses an image onto the retina. The retina has several layers, one of which contains special cells named for their shapes—rods and cones. Light-sensitive chemicals in the rods and cones react to specific wavelengths of light and trigger nerve impulses. These impulses are carried through the optic nerve to the visual center in the brain. Here they are interpreted, and sight occurs. There are about 75 to 150 million rods and about 7 million cones in the human retina.

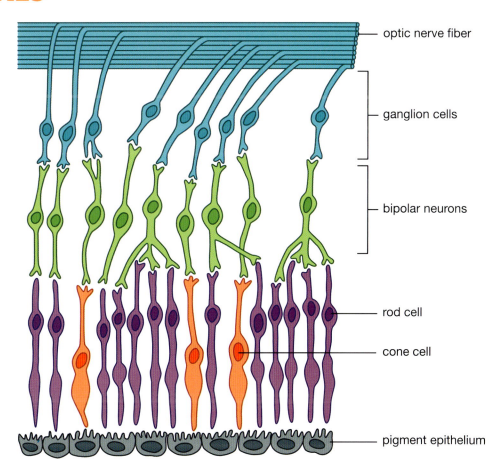

OUR EARS

Vibrations of air molecules moving through the air are received and translated into messages that the brain recognizes as sound by a complex organ—the ear. The ear has two important, but different, functions: hearing and sensing the body's equilibrium, or balance. The mechanisms for these processes are located within a hollow space in the skull's temporal bone.

PARTS OF THE EAR

The ear has three separate sections—the outer ear, the middle ear, and the inner ear. Each section performs a specific function, related to either hearing or balance.

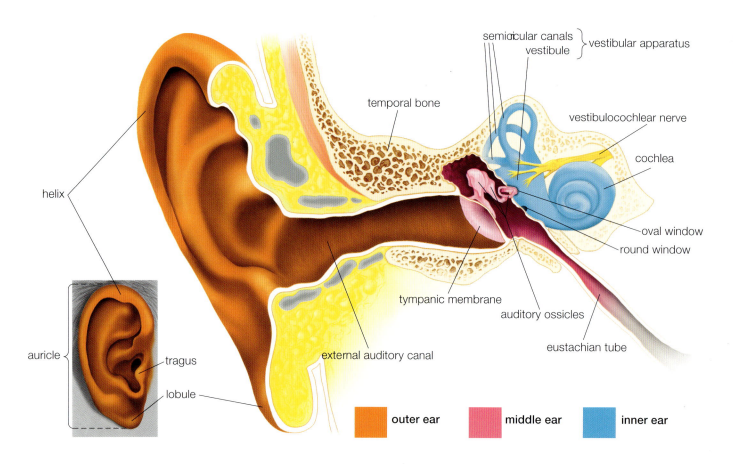

semicircular canals
vestibule
} vestibular apparatus

temporal bone

vestibulocochlear nerve

cochlea

helix

oval window

round window

tympanic membrane

auditory ossicles

eustachian tube

auricle

tragus

external auditory canal

lobule

outer ear   middle ear   inner ear

THE OUTER EAR

The outer ear is divided into two main parts: the auricle and the ear canal. The auricle is the part of the ear that is visible on the sides of the head. It is made of a tough material called cartilage. It collects sound waves and sends them into a curved passageway called the ear canal.

The ear canal leads to the eardrum, which separates the outer ear from the middle ear. The eardrum vibrates when sound hits it. It then passes the vibrations to the middle ear.

THE MIDDLE EAR

The middle ear is an air-filled space. It is about 0.75 inch (1.9 centimeters) high and 0.20 inch (0.5 centimeter) wide. Inside this space are three small bones. These bones work together to send vibrations along to the inner ear.

THE INNER EAR

The inner ear is filled with fluid. It contains the main organ of hearing, a coiled tube called the cochlea. The vibrations make waves in the fluid of the cochlea. These waves produce the sound signals that are sent to the brain. The inner ear also has structures called the semicircular canals, which help to keep the body in balance.

Structures in the inner ear help keep the body in balance.

When people fly, drive in the mountains, or swim deep underwater, their ears may "pop."

OUR HANDS

Human beings, alone in the animal kingdom, are tool makers and tool users. The ability to make and use tools depends in great part upon the use of the hands guided by the intelligence of the brain. It is believed that in the evolution of humanity the development of the brain and dexterity in the hands were mutually dependent processes.

THE STRUCTURE OF THE HAND

The human hand is located at the end of the arm, with the ball-and-socket joint at the shoulder, the hinge joint at the elbow, and a peculiar joint at the wrist. The eight bones of the wrist are called carpal bones, the five of the palm are the metacarpals, and the 14 in the fingers are the phalanges. All these bones are connected by tough flexible ligaments.

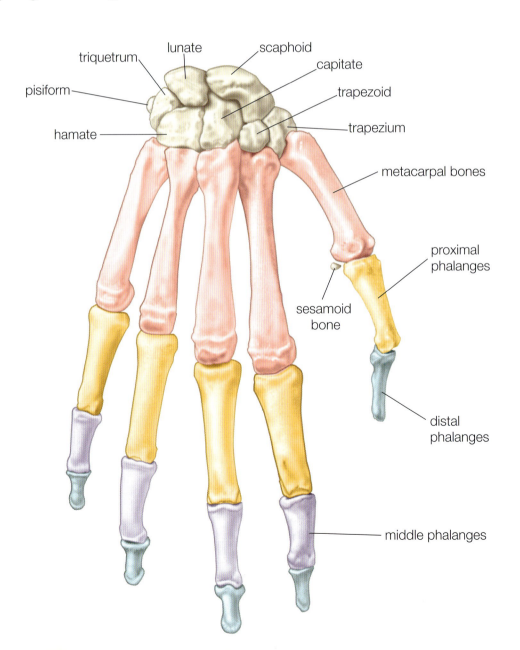

FIVE FAST FACTS

1 There are more than 30 pairs of muscles involved in producing hand motions.

2 In humans the thumb is set at an angle from the other fingers. In apes and humans it rotates on what is called the carpometacarpal joint and is therefore opposable to the other fingers. It is this feature that makes it possible to pick up and hold objects.

3 The sensitivity of the hand is more highly developed than in many other parts of the body. There are numerous little elevations or papillae on the skin of the palm, and fine nerve fibers extend from these to the brain. Thus the skin is made very sensitive to touch, heat, and cold.

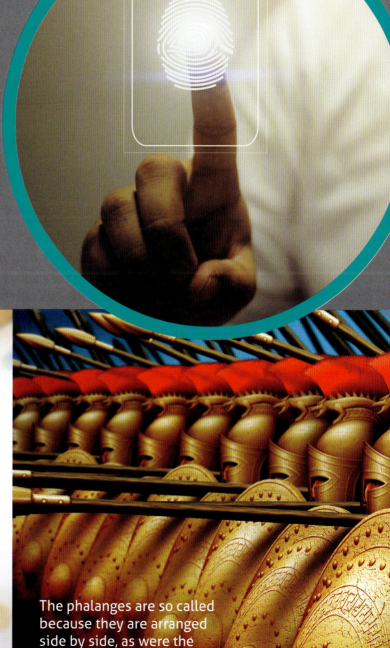

4 In primates the tips of the fingers are covered by fingernails. The palms and undersides of the fingers are marked by creases and covered by ridges called palm prints and fingerprints. These serve to increase sensitivity and gripping power.

5 Human fingerprints, because they are distinctive for each individual, are also used for identification.

The phalanges are so called because they are arranged side by side, as were the Greek soldiers in the military formation known as the phalanx.

SLEEP

Scientists are uncertain about the purpose of sleep. One theory holds that, among those animals that maintain a constant body temperature, sleep is a way to conserve energy because the body uses less energy when asleep than when awake. Another theory maintains that sleep allows the body and mind to recuperate from the day's stress and activity.

TYPES OF SLEEP

Studies of sleeping subjects, in which the electrical activity of the subjects' brains was monitored by an electroencephalograph (EEG) have shown that sleep periods are made up of two types of sleep—REM (rapid eye movement) and non-REM.

REM SLEEP

During REM sleep, the sleeper's eyes move rapidly back and forth beneath the closed eyelids. REM sleep is closely related to wakefulness—there is considerable physiological activity, body movement, and twitching. It was once thought that dreams occurred only in REM sleep, and that the sleeper's movements represented the acting out of these dreams.

NREM SLEEP

Non-REM, or NREM, sleep is of a different quality. It consists of four stages measurable by an EEG. Stage 1 is a kind of twilight between wakefulness and sleep. The pulse and respiration become more even, and the muscles relax. In Stage 2, breathing and heart rate slow. As Stage 3 is reached, breathing and heart rate continue to slow and blood pressure and body temperature fall. Stage 4 brings the deepest sleep. The muscles are completely relaxed, and the sleeper moves very little and is awakened only with difficulty. This stage is the deep, restorative, quiet sleep associated with "a good night's rest." It is now known that dreams also occur during NREM sleep.

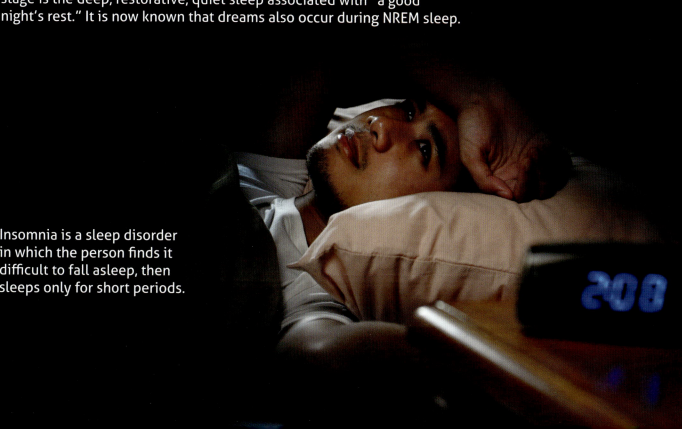

Insomnia is a sleep disorder in which the person finds it difficult to fall asleep, then sleeps only for short periods.

TEST WHAT YOU KNOW

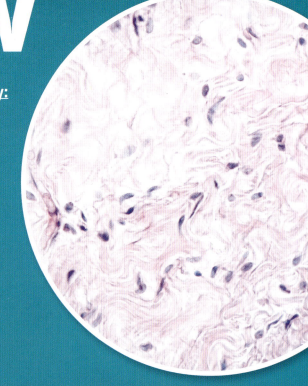

1. **There are more than 75 trillion of these in the body:**

   Cells   Neurons in the human brain

2. **Adult humans have 206 bones.**

   True   False

3. **Ligaments connect muscle to bone.**

   True   False

4. **What are the upper chambers of the heart called?**

   Atria   Venticles

5. **Which type of blood cell is most common?**

   Red   White   Platelet

6. **Human lungs never empty completely.**

   True   False

7. **The small intestine is longer than the large intestine.**

   True   False

8. **The thyroid is part of this system.**

   Nervous   Integumentary   Endocrine

9. **These nerve fibers usually conduct nerve impulses toward the cell body.**

   Axons   Dendrites

10. **Humans blink about once every thirty seconds.**

    True   False

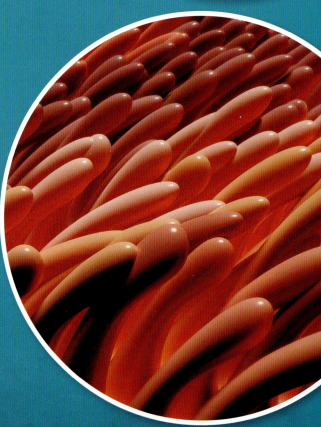